Colour the **A**. Trace the letters with your finger.

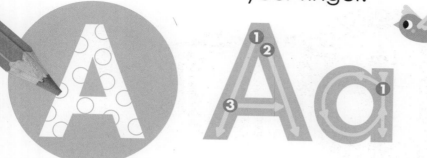

Trace the dotted letters with your pencil.

Trace the uppercase and lowercase **a**'s.

Ava

ant

Colour the **B**. Trace the letters with your finger.

Trace the dotted letters with your pencil.

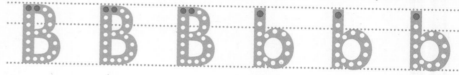

Trace the uppercase and lowercase **b**'s.

Ben

b

Colour the **C**. Trace the letters with your finger.

Trace the dotted letters with your pencil.

Trace the uppercase and lowercase **c**'s.

Chloe cactus

Colour the **D**. Trace the letters with your finger.

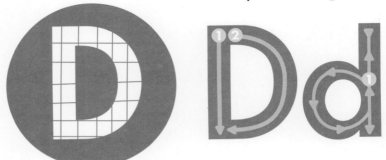

Trace the dotted letters with your pencil.

Trace the uppercase and lowercase **d**'s.

Daniel dragon

Colour the **E**. Trace the letters with your finger.

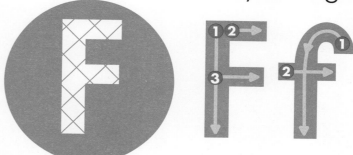

Trace the dotted letters with your pencil.

Trace the uppercase and lowercase **e**'s.

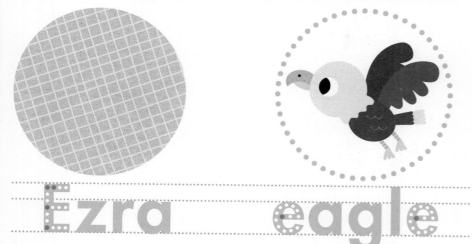

Ezra   eagle

Colour the **F**. Trace the letters with your finger.

Trace the dotted letters with your pencil.

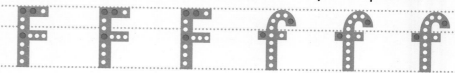

Trace the uppercase and lowercase **f**'s.

Frances   fish

Colour the **G**.   Trace the letters with your finger.

Colour the **H**.   Trace the letters with your finger.

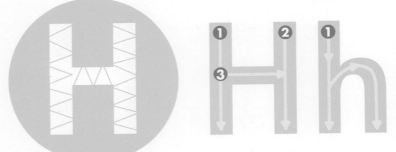

Trace the dotted letters with your pencil.

Trace the dotted letters with your pencil.

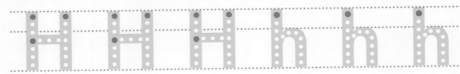

Trace the uppercase and lowercase **g**'s.

Trace the uppercase and lowercase **h**'s.

George   girl

Hazel   hen

Colour the **I**. Trace the letters with your finger.

Trace the dotted letters with your pencil.

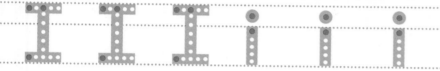

Trace the uppercase and lowercase **i**'s.

Isaac

igloo

Colour the **J**. Trace the letters with your finger.

Trace the dotted letters with your pencil.

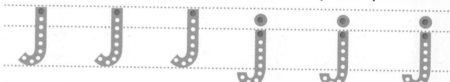

Trace the uppercase and lowercase **j**'s.

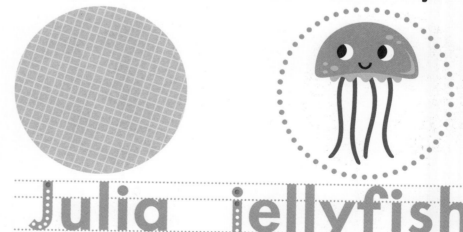

Julia jellyfish

Colour the **K**.   Trace the letters with your finger.

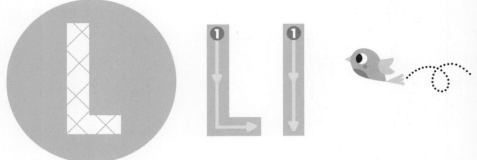

Trace the dotted letters with your pencil.

Trace the uppercase and lowercase **k**'s.

Kaia   **king**

Colour the **L**.   Trace the letters with your finger.

Trace the dotted letters with your pencil.

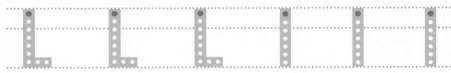

Trace the uppercase and lowercase **l**'s.

Logan   **llama**

Colour the **M**. Trace the letters with your finger.

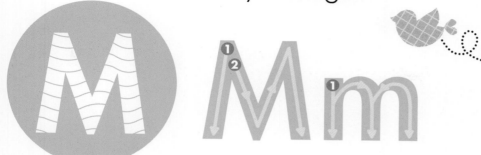

Trace the dotted letters with your pencil.

M M M m m m

Trace the uppercase and lowercase **m**'s.

Mila

milk

Colour the **N**. Trace the letters with your finger.

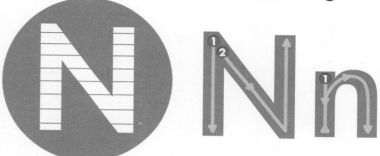

Trace the dotted letters with your pencil.

N N N n n n

Trace the uppercase and lowercase **n**'s.

Nick

necklace

Colour the **O**.   Trace the letters with your finger.

Colour the **P**.   Trace the letters with your finger.

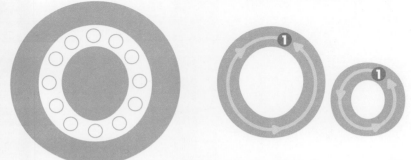

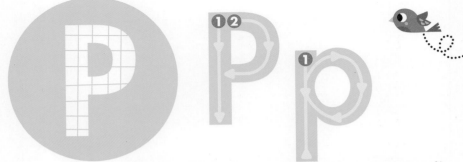

Trace the dotted letters with your pencil.

Trace the dotted letters with your pencil.

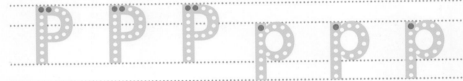

Trace the uppercase and lowercase **o**'s.

Trace the uppercase and lowercase **p**'s.

Olive   octopus

Peter   peach

Colour the **Q**. Trace the letters with your finger.

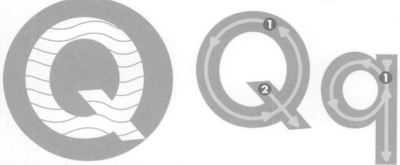

Trace the dotted letters with your pencil.

Trace the uppercase and lowercase **q**'s.

Quinn   quail

Colour the **R**. Trace the letters with your finger.

Trace the dotted letters with your pencil.

Trace the uppercase and lowercase **r**'s.

 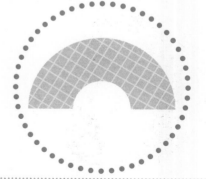

Ryan   rainbow

Colour the **S**.   Trace the letters with your finger.

Trace the dotted letters with your pencil.

Trace the uppercase and lowercase **s**'s.

 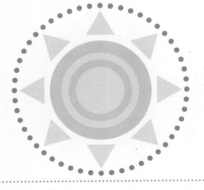

Sarah   sun

Colour the **T**.   Trace the letters with your finger.

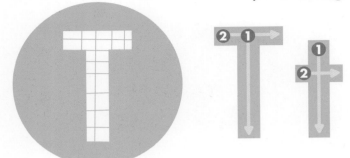

Trace the dotted letters with your pencil.

Trace the uppercase and lowercase **t**'s.

Theo   tractor

Colour the **U**. Trace the letters with your finger.

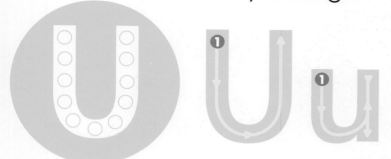

Trace the dotted letters with your pencil.

Trace the uppercase and lowercase **u**'s.

Una   unicorn

Colour the **V**. Trace the letters with your finger.

Trace the dotted letters with your pencil.

Trace the uppercase and lowercase **v**'s.

Victor   volcano

Colour the **W**.   Trace the letters with your finger.

Trace the dotted letters with your pencil.

Trace the uppercase and lowercase **w**'s.

Wyatt   walrus

Colour the **X**.   Trace the letters with your finger.

Trace the dotted letters with your pencil.

Trace the uppercase and lowercase **x**'s.

Lexie   X-ray

Colour the **Y**. Trace the letters with your finger.

Trace the dotted letters with your pencil.

Trace the uppercase and lowercase **y**'s.

Yasmine yak

Colour the **Z**. Trace the letters with your finger.

Trace the dotted letters with your pencil.

Trace the uppercase and lowercase **z**'s.

Zack zip

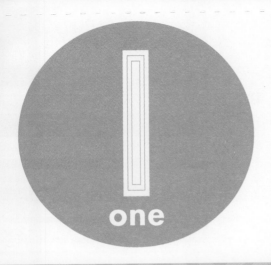

one

Colour the **1**. Then count **1** dog.

Trace **1** present.

Circle the bowl with **1** fish in it.

Trace the **1**'s with your finger and then with your pencil.

14

two

Colour the **2**. Then count **2** shoes.

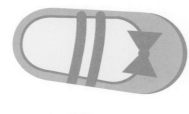
①

②

Trace **2** boats.

Circle the cone with **2** scoops.

Trace the **2**'s with your finger and then with your pencil.

2 2 2 2 2 2 2

three

Colour the **3**. Then count **3** cars.

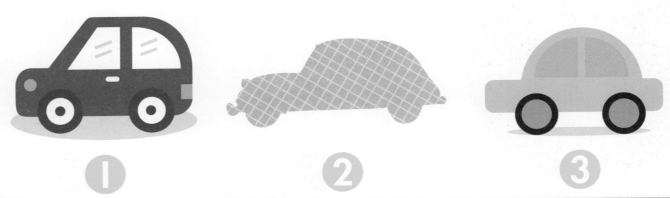

① ② ③

Trace **3** stars.

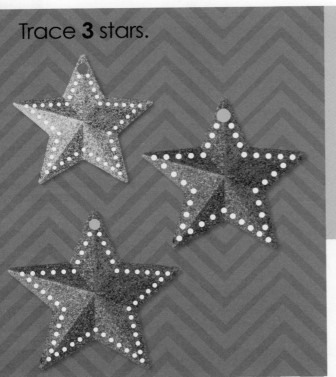

Circle the ladybird with **3** spots.

Trace the **3**'s with your finger and then with your pencil.

3 3 3 3 3 3 3 3

four

Colour the **4**. Then count **4** butterflies.

1　　2　　3　　4

Trace **4** hearts.

Colour **4** cupcakes.

Trace the **4**'s with your finger and then with your pencil.

4　4　4　4　4　4　4

Colour the **5**. Then count **5** yo-yos.

5 five

① ② ③ ④ ⑤

Trace **5** strawberries.

Count the dinosaurs in the picture.

Trace the **5**'s with your finger and then with your pencil.

5 5 5 5 5 5 5

Squares

Trace the **squares**.

Trace and colour the big square **green** and the small one **red**.

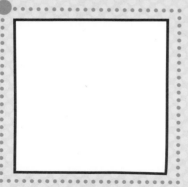 

Triangles

Trace the **triangles**.

Trace and colour the big triangles **yellow** and the small ones **blue**.

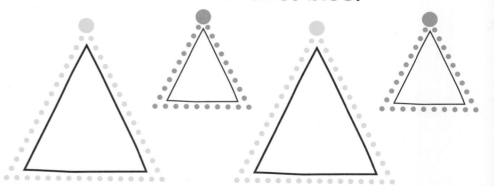

Rectangles

Trace the **rectangles**.

Trace and colour the big rectangle pink and the small one **brown**.

Circles

Trace the **circles**.

Trace and colour the big circles orange and the small ones purple.

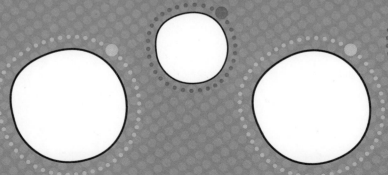

Hearts

Stars

Trace the **hearts**.

Trace the **stars**.

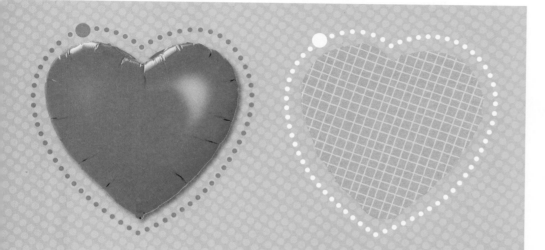

Trace and colour the big heart **red** and the small one **green**.

Trace and colour the big star **yellow** and the small one **purple**.

Ovals

Trace the ovals.

Trace and colour the big ovals **pink** and the small ovals **blue**.

Arrows

Trace the arrows.

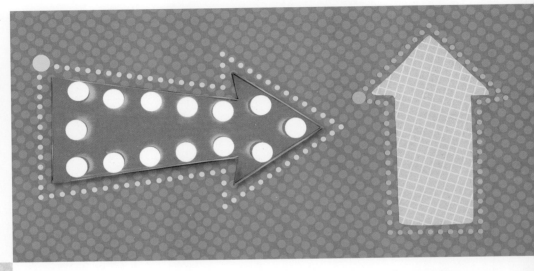

Trace and colour the big arrow **brown** and the small one **yellow**.

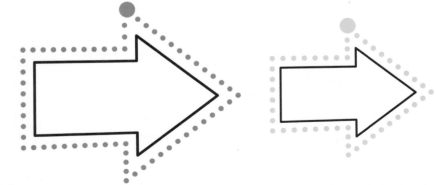

What's different?

Circle the kitten that is different.

Circle the butterfly that is different.

Match the pairs

Draw lines to join the pictures that are the same.

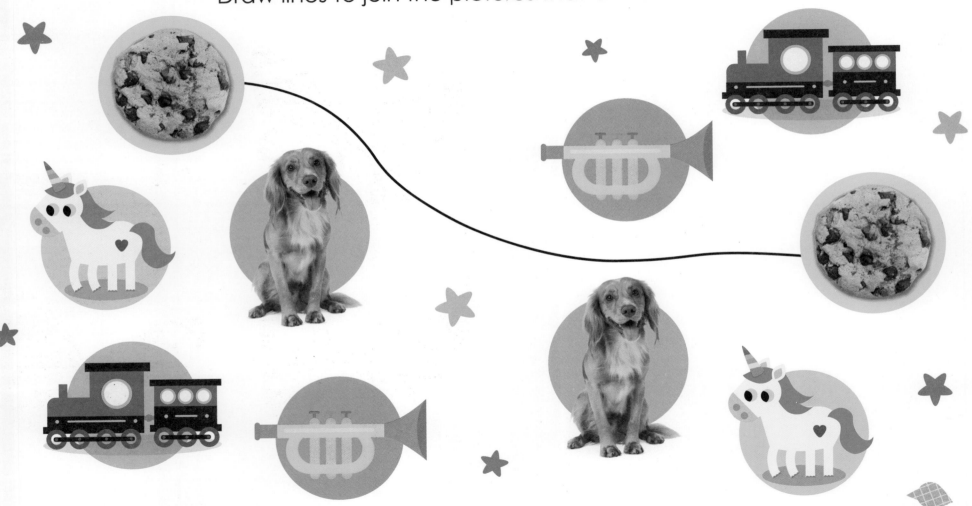

Put them away

Draw a line from each toy to the correct box.

dolls

books

bears

Red

Trace these **red** things.

Colour these things **red**.

Green

Trace these **green** things.

Colour these things **green**.

Blue

Trace these **blue** things.

Orange

Trace these orange things.

Colour these things **blue**.

Colour these things **orange**.

Yellow

Trace these yellow things.

Colour these things yellow.

Purple

Trace these purple things.

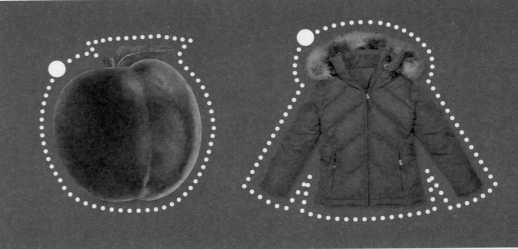

Colour these things purple.

Pink

 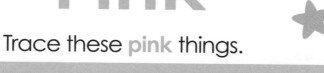 

Trace these **pink** things.

Colour these things **pink**.

Brown

Trace these **brown** things.

Colour these things **brown**.

Black

Trace these **black** things.

Colour these things **black**.

White

Trace these **white** things.

Trace these **white** things.